of elves and fairies. Everyone who lives here is very, very small.

Contents Page

This annual is packed full of elf and fairy fun! Don't forget to ask a grown-up to help before you start making and baking.

Published 2012.
Pedigree Books Limited, Beech Hill House, Walnut Gardens, Exeter, Devon EX4 4DH
www.pedigreebooks.com | books@pedigreegroup.co.uk

£7.99

Somewhere, hidden amongst thorny brambles, is a little Kingdom

Ben, Holly and their best friend Gaston are going to play in the Little Kingdom.

Would you like to play, too?

"WOOF!"

"WOOF!"

6

Ben & Holly's Little Kingdom™

This annual belongs to

....

Draw your portrait here

Ben Elf

My name's Ben and I'm an elf! Elves are good at making things, but we definitely don't do magic. I live with my mum, dad and all the other elves in the Great Elf Tree.

Colour Me

Colour in my picture. Can you guess what am I blowing? Draw the dots to find out!

8

Meet Ben!

I have lots of adventures in the Little Kingdom with my best friend Holly. We've explored ant hills, met witches and taken trips to the seaside. We've even been to the Moon and back!

Lots to learn at Elf School

I go to Elf School every day. The classroom is right at the very top of the Great Elf Tree! At Elf School, the Wise Old Elf teaches us how to make toys.

What else happens at Elf School? Tick the sentences that are right. Put a cross next to the ones that are wrong.

1. Flying and spells are allowed in class.

2. Lots of pictures are pinned up on the walls.

3. The pupils sit at little wooden desks.

4. The Wise Old Elf wears a funny pink hat.

5. Elves learn to make clockwork owls, rabbits and robots.

What toy would you like to make at Elf School?

Draw it in here.

9

Princess Holly

I'm a fairy princess called Holly! I live in the Little Castle, but every day I come out to play with my best friend Ben. I have a magic wand for casting spells and a pair of fluttery fairy wings.

Colour in my picture. What shall I magic up with my wand today? Draw something surprising!

Colour Me

Meet Holly!

I live with my mummy, daddy, and my twin sisters Daisy and Poppy. Nanny Plum helps look after us. If any of my spells go wrong, Nanny Plum tries to sort things out again.

Magical Mix-ups

Even when my spells don't turn out quite right, Ben and I always end up giggling in the end! Draw a line to match the magical pictures to the funny things that have happened. Oops!

1. Magic brushes splodged paint all over the kitchen.

2. Ben got turned into a frog.

3. The Little Castle was flooded with ice cream.

4. Poor Betty Caterpillar got whooshed up into the air.

A

B

C

D

'Abraca zobbedy zoo' are my favourite spell words.

What are yours?

Gaston

Gaston the Ladybird is Ben and Holly's favourite playmate! He lives in his own little cave not far away from the Elf Windmill. Gaston loves to roll on his back and wiggle his legs in the air.

Can you finish Gaston's picture? Only one important colour is missing. Which is it?

Colour Me

12

Meet Gaston!

Gaston is a very clever Ladybird - he is especially good at fetching sticks. He also has wings just like Holly. When Ben needs to go extra-fast, Gaston gives the elf a lift on his back!

Cave Counting

Gaston's little cave is very messy, but that's just the way he likes it. Look at all cobwebs, apple cores and smelly socks! Count up the objects and write the number in each box.

Cobwebs ☐

Apple Cores ☐

Magazines ☐

Licked Lollies ☐

Smelly Socks ☐

Gaston has lost his food bowl in all the mess! Can you spot it?

A Wander in the Woods

Nanny Plum has taken Ben and Holly to visit someone very mysterious! Nanny Plum says that the person is old and a bit smelly. They also drink sour milk and nibble on worm cakes!

Who are Ben and Holly visiting today? Join up the dots and then colour the mysterious person in.

Put a tick next to the right name.

Mr Gnome ☐
The Wise Old Elf ☐
Mrs Witch ☐

Colour Me

14

Musical Statues

Daisy and Poppy are having a party! Look at the children playing musical statues.
Who is the best at standing still? Tarquin, Raspberry or Nettle Elf?

Only one guest wobbled during the game. Colour in the balloon next to the right party picture.

A

B

C

D

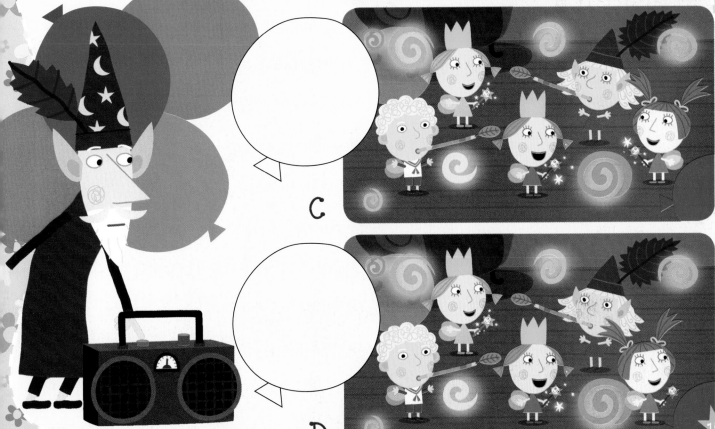

King and Queen Thistle

King and Queen Thistle are very busy fairies indeed. As well as being Holly, Daisy and Poppy's mummy and daddy, they rush around the Little Kingdom doing important royal work.

Colour Me

Colour in the King and Queen sitting on their thrones. Use the little picture to help you choose the right colours for the big picture.

Meet King and Queen Thistle!

King and Queen Thistle are always being asked to launch boats, judge competitions and make speeches. Sometimes the King would much rather read his newspaper or go on picnics with Ben and Holly.

The Royal Fairy Picnic

It's the perfect day for a royal fairy picnic! King and Queen Thistle fancy sandwiches, sparkling fairy juice and a bowlful of magic jelly*! Draw a circle around all the things that the fairies might need for their trip out.

*No one wants another jelly flood! Draw a scrummy bowl of magic jelly in here.

A Very Busy Day

King Thistle has got a very busy day planned! Nanny Plum has written everything down so that he won't forget any of his appointments.

TO DO

9 o'clock

Wave a lot in the royal car

11 o'clock

Launch an elf boat

2 o'clock

Judge a fairy fruit and vegetable competition

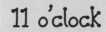

4 o'clock

Make a speech at the Festival of Elf and Fairy Dancing

The King must never be late! Can you draw the big and little hands on the clock faces? Use Nanny Plum's list to help you show the right time for each royal appointment.

A Fairy Feast

Look who's come to dinner at the Little Castle! King and Queen Marigold are terribly posh, but even they can't resist Nanny Plum's cooking. Everyone agrees that Nanny Plum's suppers are much nicer than modern food.

Nanny Plum has lost her wand. Where is it?

How many elves are there?

How many fairies are sat around the kitchen table?

Think of a name for Nanny Plum's recipe.

....

The Royal Golf Course

King Thistle was teaching Ben and Holly to play golf.
"It is simple really," he explained. "You just hit the ball into the hole."

Ben and Holly thought crazy golf would be more fun. In crazy golf, you got to knock your balls up hills and round corners.

Boom! Rumble! Boom!

Daddy must have magicked them!

Suddenly a giant hill pushed its way out of the ground. Another then another one popped up beside it.
King Thistle looked cross. "I didn't magic these hills," he said.
Soon there were hills everywhere!

1

The King marched down the hill to find the Wise Old Elf.
"Who made these hills?" he demanded.
"A mole, your Majesty," replied the Wise Old Elf.

The Wise Old Elf and his elves had been trying to chase the mole away all morning.
"Nanny Plum will know what to do," said Ben. "She speaks all animal languages!" agreed Holly.

Well, get rid of it!

King Thistle summoned Nanny Plum.
"I can't speak Mole," she admitted.
The only magical method to get rid of a mole was to use a gnome.

I'll fetch us a gnome!

"Gnomes eat too much, talk too much and never do any work," moaned the Wise Old Elf.

"Hello Mr Gnome," said Nanny Plum.
"I've called you here to get rid of
some moles."
The gnome got out a little guitar
and started to strum.

I like trees, they're not like peas, Custard Creams on goo!

As soon as it heard the gnome's tune,
the mole ran out of its hole.

"Thank you!" beamed King Thistle.
"How much do I owe you?"

My tummy is
very empty!

The gnome asked the King for
some elf workers and lots and
lots of food.

"Wise Old Elf," said the King.
"Do whatever the gnome says!"

2

"The first job is to flatten these hills." said the gnome. "And build a windmill."
The elves got to work.
The gnome asked Ben and Holly to fetch him a deckchair and a fishing rod.

Once the hills were flat, the Wise Old Elf started building the gnome's windmill.
Ben and Holly brought sandwiches, tea, a deckchair and fishing rod for the gnome.

"Why is it a 'pretend' windmill?" asked Holly.
"The gnome said it mustn't actually work," said the Wise Old Elf.

Ben and Holly helped paint the windmill and fix the sails.

Ben and Holly went to tell the gnome that the windmill was ready. The hungry gnome asked Ben and Holly to fetch him even more food! "I also need a little bridge, a plastic well and a picket fence," ordered the gnome.

> I also need some plastic flowers!

Back at the Little Castle, Nanny Plum was cross. The gnome had eaten all the food in her kitchen!

The Royal Golf Course was covered with plastic flowers, windmills and picket fences!

The gnome lazily opened an eye.
"Thank you Wise Old Elf," he nodded. "I couldn't have done a better job myself."

> We've made everything you asked for.

> Snuffle, SNORE!

26

The King decided that it was time for the gnome to leave. "I might have to stay here forever," said the gnome, who then ate jar of pickles, then gave a great, big BURP and went to sleep.

"What about my golf?" blubbed the King. Ben and Holly thought the new golf course looked like fun.

King Thistle shook his head. "I can't play golf with all this stuff around," he sighed. "Just hit the ball through the little windmill..." said Holly.

"...and into the hole!" finished Ben. King Thistle chuckled. Crazy golf was fun after all!

Ben & Holly's Little Kingdom™

Daisy and Poppy

Daisy and Poppy are Princess Holly's little fairy sisters. They are not very good at flying or magic yet, but they like practicing! Holly thinks the twins are a bit naughty, but sometimes she lets them play with her.

> Use the numbers to help you choose the crayons or pencils you need to finish this fairy picture.

Colour Me

Meet Daisy and Poppy!

Princess Daisy and Princess Poppy can't resist playing with other fairies' wands. Once they turned Holly's friend Fleur into a little black kitten and Mr and Mrs Elf into rabbits!

Babies' Bedtime

After a busy day of magical mischief, Daisy and Poppy have fallen fast asleep. Look carefully at the picture then fill the paint splats with the right colours.

The colour of Daisy and Poppy's crowns is

The colour of their toybox is

The colour of the princesses' bed is

The colour of Daisy and Poppy's duvet is

What are Daisy and Poppy day dreaming about?

Draw a picture in here.

29

Make Your Own Little Kingdom

Everything in the Little Kingdom is very, very small. It is hidden away amongst thorny brambles, out of the sight of boys and girls. Would you like to make a Little Kingdom to keep in your bedroom? All you need are a few teeny bits and bobs and a BIG imagination!

Scissors are sharp!

Ask a grown-up to help you do the cutting.

You will need:

* An empty shoebox
* Old newspapers
* Paint
* Paint brushes
* Coloured paper
* Scissors
* PVA glue
* Tissue paper
* Silver foil
* Twigs, shells, pebbles and other craft supplies

Step 1

Take the lid off the shoebox and keep it safe. Paint the bottom of the box all over in green paint. Put the shoe box on some old newspapers to dry.

You don't need magic to make this Little Kingdom. Making things is elf work!

When you've finished making your Little Kingdom, use paints and crayons to decorate the lid. Writing your name on the top in pretty fairy colours will make the box look extra magical!

30

Step 2

Find a sheet of green paper and cut out two round shapes. One is going to be the Meadow and the other will be the Royal Golf Course.

Make flags for my golf course out of triangles of coloured paper. You could even ask a grown-up to wrap the paper around cocktail sticks to make flagpoles!

Step 3

When the shoe box is dry, take the Meadow and the Royal Golf Course shapes and stick them inside. Scrunch up little pieces of yellow and white tissue paper to make flowers, then stick them on the Meadow shape.

Step 4

Cut out a circle of silver foil and stick it in the corner to make the Frog Pond.

Step 5

Scrunch up more pieces of green tissue and stick them around the edge to make the trees that grow around the Little Kingdom.

Don't forget to make the Little Castle, too! Try using a matchbox with a plastic bottle lid on top.

Step 6

Now it's time to make the houses - how you do it depends on what you can find in your craft drawer and outside in your garden! What about painting a smooth pebble to make Gaston's house, or fixing a twig in place as the Great Elf Tree?

Chicken Run

Ben Elf and Holly are going out to fetch an egg for King Thistle's breakfast. Mr Elf will have to drive the elf truck all the way through the Elf Farm until they reach the chicken coop. Can you help him find the right road?

Collecting chicken eggs is very difficult, even for fairies and elves! Put your finger on the start, then follow the path in and out of the vegetable patches. If you reach a big frilly lettuce or a shiny tomato, turn back and try another route.

START

A Pet for the Princesses

Daisy and Poppy really want a pony, but ponies are ginormous! What other sort of animal could the princesses look after?

King Thistle says that the twins can have a pet as long as it is small and fluffy.

Draw a circle around the right pet for the fairy princesses. Make sure that it is the smallest and fluffiest one on the page.

A. A Ladybird

B. A Hamster

Which pet did you choose?

C. A Crow

D. A Kitten

Look what pet the lucky princesses ended up with in the end.
Pippin the pony is even bigger than the Little Castle!

Would you love to have a new pet? Draw a picture of your pet in here. You can imagine any creature you like, even a dragon!

Nature Class Quiz

Today the elves are having a joint nature class with the fairies! In nature class, the children learn the names of trees, mushrooms and frogs. It is very important that everyone pays attention to the Wise Old Elf and Nanny Plum.

Would you get top marks in nature class? Draw a circle around the right answers.

1

What does an acorn grow into?

a. a rose bush
b. an oak tree
c. a fir tree

2

What type of mushroom this?

a. a toadstool
b. a rosehip
c. clover

3

What white flowers grow in the Meadow?

a. daisies
b. carnations
c. buttercups

4

Which of these does not grow in the Little Kingdom?

a. thistles
b. brambles
c. cactus

5

What animal is this?

a. a frog
b. a newt
c. a chicken

BEDTIME
Reading

Picnic To The Moon

This adventure starts at the little castle...

"The elves want you to inspect their latest toy," Nanny Plum announced one morning.

King Thistle sighed. He really wanted to read his newspaper.

"I don't like these elf toy inspections," he grumbled.

"The toys are always perfect."

There was no getting out of it. The elf truck had already arrived.

The King and Holly went out to meet Mr Elf and Ben.

"May I present the very latest elf toy," said Mr Elf proudly. "A space rocket!"

The rocket lifted up into the air, then parachuted back to the ground. Pouf!

"Is that it?" said King Thistle. "I could kick a football higher than that!"

Mr Elf looked a bit upset.

"It is just a toy your majesty."

King Thistle was not
impressed with the elf toy.
"Rockets should be able
to go higher than
footballs," he argued.
"I could make a rocket go to the
Moon," insisted Mr Elf.
"If I wanted to..."
"I bet you can't fly Holly, Ben,
Gaston, me and Nanny Plum to the Moon by
tonight,"said the King.
Me Elf gulped. He needed to start work
on a new rocket. It was a matter of
elf honour!

When the Wise Old Elf heard about the
King's bet, he thought it was impossible.
But, if elf honour was at stake, the rocket
had to be built! He put all the elves in the
toy factory on the job.

"Now," he mumbled, "I just need to
work out how to get it from the Little
Kingdom to the Moon."

As soon as it got dark, Mr Elf phoned King Thistle.

"Hello your majesty," he said, proudly. "The elf rocket is ready!"

The King was impressed.

"That was quick!"

The fairies packed a picnic, then rushed out to Elf Oak Wood. The Wise Old Elf showed them a map of the Moon.

"The rocket will land here," he explained, "in the Sea of Tranquility."

"We can build sandcastles!" cheered Holly.

"And have a picnic on the beach," piped up Nanny Plum.

Wise Old Elf shook his head. The Sea of Tranquility wasn't a real sea. There wasn't any water on the Moon!

"This is a very serious mission," he frowned, showing everyone on board.

Even though the rocket was very big, its passenger cabin was very small.

"I might stay below in the kitchen," decided Nanny Plum.

"There isn't a kitchen or a toilet," replied the Wise Old Elf. "The space below is for fuel."

There wasn't any time to argue. The astronauts needed to get ready for take-off!

Everyone got changed into space suits and helmets. All the fairies were told to hand in their wands. Magic was not allowed on board the elf rocket.

When the astronauts were strapped in, the elves in the mission control room did a systems check.

"Start the countdown!" cried the Wise Old Elf.

10! 9! 8! 7! 6! 5! 4! 3! 2! 1!

"Here we go!"cried Ben.

Holly giggled. "Next stop, the Moon!" Wise Old Elf and Queen Thistle watched the rocket rumble and shake.

"BLAST OFF!"

The rocket roared up into the night sky.
The Wise Old Elf rubbed his eyes.
"It actually worked," he gasped.
"I wasn't expecting that."

On board, Mr Elf grinned. This mission
was going exceedingly well.

"We are now out of the Earth's
atmosphere," he declared. "We can take
off our seatbelts."
Even though her wings weren't
flapping, Holly began to float. Zero
gravity was fun!
"What's through here?" asked Nanny
Plum, opening a door with a no entry sign.
"Are you sure there isn't a toilet?"
Suddenly all the air swooshed out of
the rocket, taking Nanny Plum with it!
"Hang on!" shouted Mr Elf.
Too late! Nanny Plum was floating into
deep space.

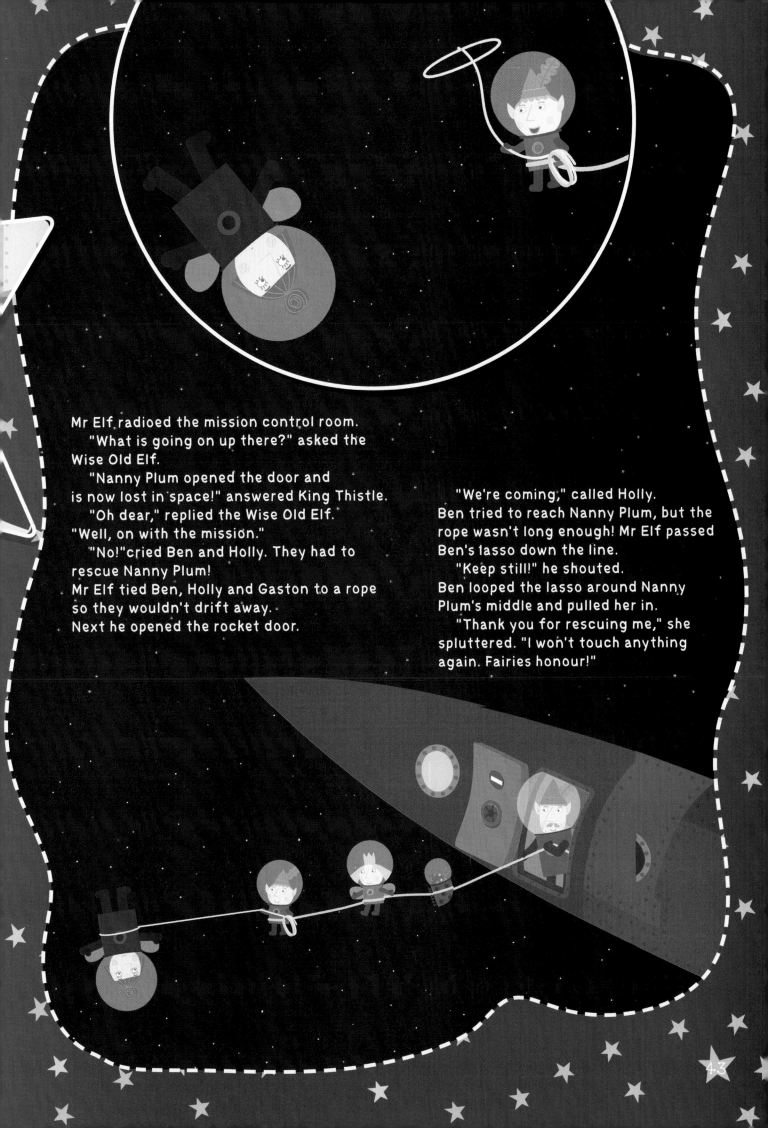

Mr Elf radioed the mission control room.
"What is going on up there?" asked the
Wise Old Elf.
"Nanny Plum opened the door and
is now lost in space!" answered King Thistle.
"Oh dear," replied the Wise Old Elf.
"Well, on with the mission."
"No!"cried Ben and Holly. They had to
rescue Nanny Plum!
Mr Elf tied Ben, Holly and Gaston to a rope
so they wouldn't drift away.
Next he opened the rocket door.

"We're coming," called Holly.
Ben tried to reach Nanny Plum, but the
rope wasn't long enough! Mr Elf passed
Ben's lasso down the line.
"Keep still!" he shouted.
Ben looped the lasso around Nanny
Plum's middle and pulled her in.
"Thank you for rescuing me," she
spluttered. "I won't touch anything
again. Fairies honour!"

Once Nanny Plum was safely back inside, Mr Elf set a course for the Moon.

"You are on target to land in the Sea of Tranquility," radioed the Wise Old Elf from mission control.

"Lovely," beamed Nanny Plum. "Once we're at the seaside we'll need to eat our picnic."

Mr Elf sighed. "For the last time, we are NOT going for a picnic! This is a serious elf mission to the Moon."

"We can still have a picnic," sniffed Nanny Plum.

A few minutes' later, the elf rocket touched down on the surface of the Moon. The astronauts climbed out.

"Look how high I can jump!" squealed Holly. Ben bounced past her.

"This is brilliant!"

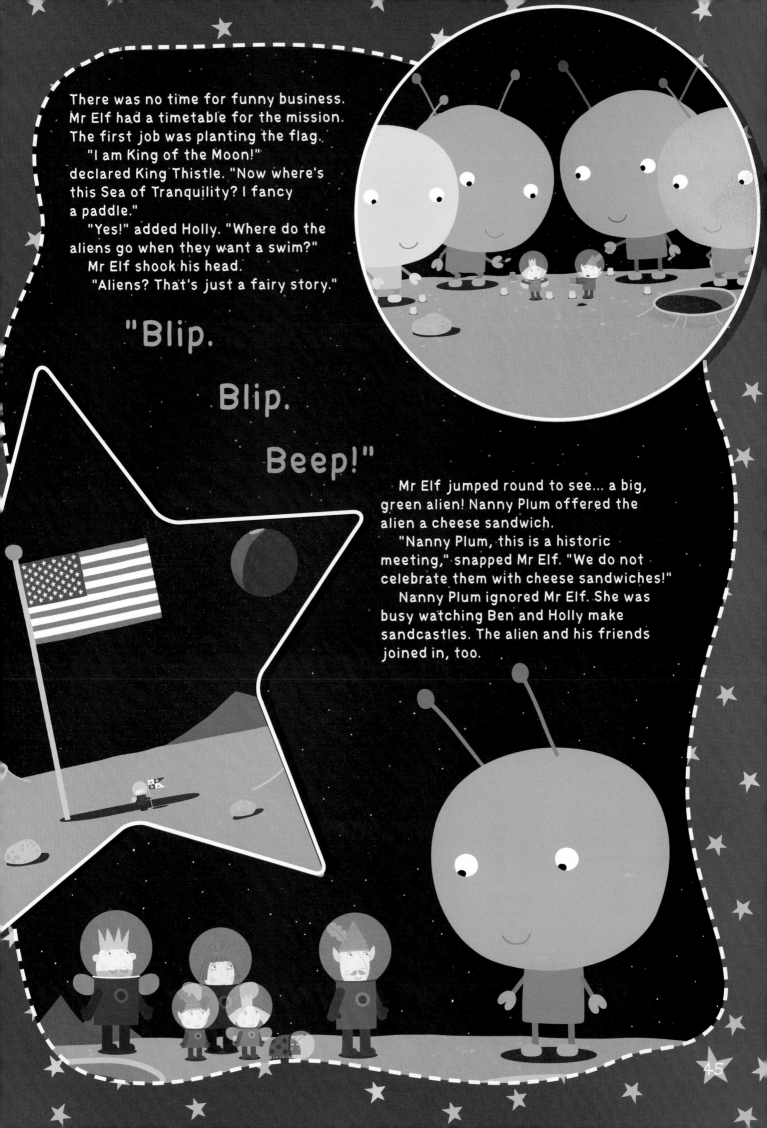

There was no time for funny business. Mr Elf had a timetable for the mission. The first job was planting the flag.

"I am King of the Moon!" declared King Thistle. "Now where's this Sea of Tranquility? I fancy a paddle."

"Yes!" added Holly. "Where do the aliens go when they want a swim?"

Mr Elf shook his head.

"Aliens? That's just a fairy story."

"Blip.

Blip.

Beep!"

Mr Elf jumped round to see... a big, green alien! Nanny Plum offered the alien a cheese sandwich.

"Nanny Plum, this is a historic meeting," snapped Mr Elf. "We do not celebrate them with cheese sandwiches!"

Nanny Plum ignored Mr Elf. She was busy watching Ben and Holly make sandcastles. The alien and his friends joined in, too.

Ben rubbed his tummy. He was getting
a bit hungry.

"Time for the picnic!" said Nanny Plum.
Back at the mission control room, the Wise
Old Elf panicked.

"You can't go waving a magic wand
around!" he cried.
Nanny Plum didn't need a wand. She had
brought her magic basket!

"Magic basket please, make us
sandwiches with ham and cheese!"

Next, Nanny Plum magicked up some
pudding. Wobbly magic jelly began to pour
out of the basket.

"What is it doing?" shouted Mr. Elf. Jelly
was glooping everywhere!

Nanny Plum frowned. "I forgot to say
'not a lot'!"

"Aaagh!" bellowed King Thistle.

"JELLY FLOOD!"

The Wise Old Elf stared at his computer screen. The surface of the Moon was covered in magic jelly.

"The Sea of Tranquility will now be the Sea of Jelly," he groaned. "The aliens will be very upset."

Luckily the aliens weren't upset at all. They thought the jelly tasted delicious!

Nanny Plum tried to eat some jelly too, but her helmet got in the way.

"What kind of picnic is this?" she moaned.

"This is NOT a picnic!" snapped Mr Elf. Nanny Plum and King Thistle decided that it was time to go home.

The Wise Old Elf had a brilliant idea.
  "Nanny Plum," he radioed. "I want you to put the magic basket into the fuel tank."
  "But you said no more magic jelly!" insisted Nanny Plum.
  "There's no time for questions," replied the Wise Old Elf. "You've ran out of fuel and this is an emergency."

For once, Nanny Plum did as she was told. She put the magic basket in the fuel tank and asked for a LOT of jelly. The jelly came out of the basket so fast, it blasted the rocket up into the sky!

  The aliens were over the moon.
  "Blip, Blip," they beeped, licking up the jelly.
  "Elf rocket to control," said Mr Elf. "We are heading back to the Little Kingdom!"

The mission control room cheered. The astronauts were on their way home!

"Please land the elf rocket in the Frog Pond," radioed the Wise Old Elf.

Mr Elf pressed a special button. "Right-ho!"

Mrs Elf and Queen Thistle rushed over to the Frog Pond.

"Welcome back Ben and Holly," they cried.

King Thistle declared the mission a complete success.

"Thanks to the wonders of elf cleverness!" said the Wise Old Elf.

"Thanks to my magic jelly, you mean," added Nanny Plum.

"Let's not argue," winked the King.

"Let's just say that elf skill got us to the Moon and fairy magic got us home!"

The End

Alien Hide and Seek

Aliens love meeting fairies and elves! Before Ben and Holly went home from their picnic on the Moon, they shared a giggly game of hide and seek with their new alien friends.

There are ten cheeky aliens hiding amongst the Moon's sandy craters. Try and spot every one.

Every time you find a new alien, trace over a number with your pencil or crayon.

1 2 3 4 5

6 7 8 9 10

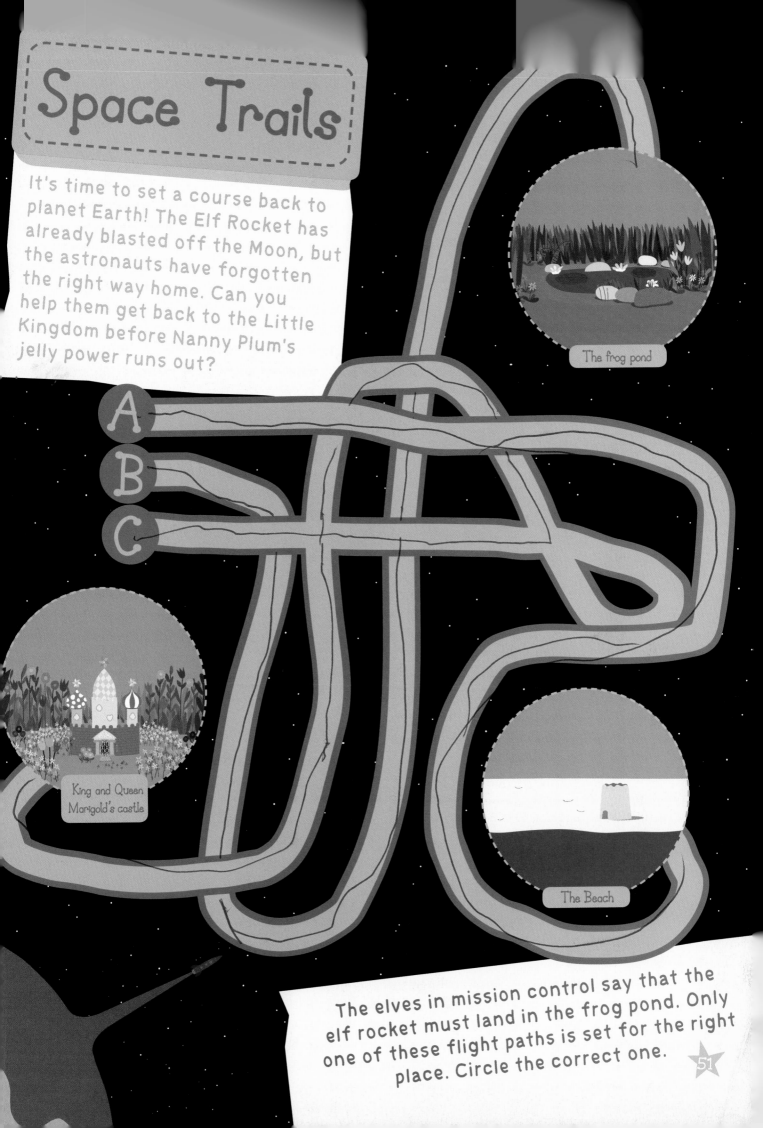

Space Trails

It's time to set a course back to planet Earth! The Elf Rocket has already blasted off the Moon, but the astronauts have forgotten the right way home. Can you help them get back to the Little Kingdom before Nanny Plum's jelly power runs out?

A

B

C

The frog pond

King and Queen Marigold's castle

The Beach

The elves in mission control say that the elf rocket must land in the frog pond. Only one of these flight paths is set for the right place. Circle the correct one.

Once Upon A Fairy Tale...

Ben and Holly love books! They both think that stories about witches, wizards and dragons are the best. When the friends run out of books to read at home, they go to the Great Elf Library to find some more.

Would you like to write a brand new story for Ben and Holly to read? Find your favourite pen, then fill the page with your own exciting fairy tale. You don't have to write words, you can tell the stories in pictures if you want to.

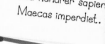

Once upon a time...

Sed scelerisque mi ac
tortor mattis pharet.
Duis tellus ante, fend
accumsan et, Totoro

Suspendisse tincidunt
sem at lorem. Aenean
vitae risus nec urna
euismod elementum.
Vestibulum ante ipsum.

Not all books have stories in them, some
are crammed full of fascinating facts.
They can tell you where the North Pole
is, how trains work and where stars go
in the daytime!

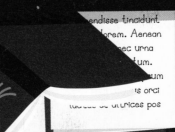

Mr and Mrs Elf

Mr and Mrs Elf are Ben's mum and dad. Ben's dad works all day driving the elf truck that delivers food to the Little Castle. Ben's mum is very good at doing lots and lots of things.

Look at Mr and Mrs Elf playing in the Elf band! Colour in the instruments they need for their oompa-oompa music.

Colour Me

Meet Mr and Mrs Elf!

Mr and Mrs Elf live in the Great Elf Tree with Ben and all the other elves. At the bottom of an escalator underneath the tree is the elf factory. No magic is allowed anywhere in the Great Elf Tree.

Let's make a Great Elf Tree picture

1. Draw a large tree trunk shape onto a sheet of brown paper and cut it out. Make sure that the shape has branches just like the Great Elf Tree. Ask a grown-up to mount the trunk onto a big piece of coloured card.

2. Place your hand on piece of green paper and spread out your fingers. Trace around the edge of your hand with a pencil. Do this lots of times until you have at least 10 hand shapes. Cut each one out.

3. Stick your hand shapes onto your picture to make the Great Elf Tree's bushy green leaves.

4. Find some crayons or pencils and draw a red front door and some little windows. Cut the pictures out and stick them onto the tree trunk of the Great Elf Tree.

5. Put your picture up on the wall for everyone to see!

Why not stick on drawings of Mr and Mrs Elf and Ben looking out of the windows?

Scissors are sharp!

Ask a grown-up to help you do the cutting.

The Elf Games

Who is standing on the podium?

The Elf Games take place every year – Ben has been in training for weeks! The Elf Games are not meant to be fun, they are very serious. Last year Ben won a trophy for the high jump.

It's Ben's turn to do the high jump. Draw in a picture of him flipping over the pole.

START

Ben and Holly are both very good at making wheelbarrows! Draw a line from the start to the end of the race.

The rulebook says that no magic or flying is allowed at the Elf Games. The Games are not for fairies*.

Jumping ☑
Running ☑
Lifting ☑
Magic ☐
Spells ☐

*If Holly can't do magic or flying, there's lots of other things she can do. She's also good at dancing, gymnastics and looking pretty. Maybe the Wise Old Elf will let her do that at the Games next year?

Ben has made a good start in the running race. What place is his friend Barnaby Elf in? Point to the elf in fourth place.

Count up the elf athletes.

Point to the elf flag.

END

The Wise Old Elf is going to present this golden trophy to the winners of the wheelbarrow race. Colour it in.

57

Big Bad Barry

"I fancy fish and chips," declared King Thistle one morning.
"We don't have any fish your Majesty," replied Nanny Plum,
"but I can magic up fish fingers!"

"I want fresh fish, from the lake," said King Thistle
"Ben's dad has a fishing boat," cried Holly.

At the lake, Ben and his dad were putting their boat, Bunty, away for winter.
Mr Elf was about to tell his son the story of Big Bad Barry The Fish when....

King Thistle arrived and he r-e-a-l-l-y wanted a fish supper.

"Let's get going!"called King Thistle
"Hang on a minute," said Mr Elf.
"You might be king on land, but on this
boat I'm in charge!"

King Thistle agreed to do as he was told,
as long Mr Elf promised they'd get a fish.
"Take the wheel," nodded Mr Elf.

Let me
have a go!

Be quiet. Fish
don't like noise.

I'll do
the steering!

Bunty

"Fishing is a tricky business," said
Mr Elf, fixing a piece of stale bread
onto the line.
"Stale bread?" gawped the King.
"Who likes that?"

King Thistle hooked a fish
straightaway!
"It must be the biggest fish in the
lake!"grinned Ben.
Mr Elf threw the fish back in the
water. "I've seen bigger."

"It was many years ago that I met Big Bad Barry," whispered Mr Elf. "Who's that?" asked Holly. Mr Elf sat down. "Only the biggest, hugest, most gigantic-est fish the world has ever seen."

"...I was out sailing in my favourite boat Hilda when I first saw Big Bad Barry. I knew I had to catch him," said Mr Elf.

It was a dark and stormy night!

Barry is still out there... somewhere.

Mr Elf explained how Big Bad Barry had eaten the cheese bait, then munched through his poor boat Hilda!
"I tried to catch Barry many more times," he added,

"but he was always too strong" King Thistle rummaged in the royal picnic basket and pulled a lump of cheese.
"I refuse to help!" cried Mr Elf.
"It's mutiny on the Bunty!"

"I'm taking charge!" declared King Thistle, putting on Mr Elf's hat. "We'll catch Big Bad Barry and have him with chips."
The King put a piece of Stilton on his hook and dangled it over the side of the boat.

Here Barry! Come on, boy!

You wanted to meet Big Bad Barry. Now's your chance.

"Excellent!" smiled King Thistle as the whiffy bait dropped into the water.
"Now we wait," added Mr Elf.
"But not for long."
Down at the bottom of the lake, someone had smelled the cheese...

A giant fish burst out of the water, leaping right over the boat!
"It's him!" bellowed Mr Elf.
"It's Big Bad Barry!"
King Thistle licked his lips.

"We'll be eating fish for a week!"
Big Bad Barry had gulped down the fishing line, cheese and all!
"Now he's pulling us backwards," shouted the King.

"RRoooaaarrr!"

Start the engine!

He's eating the line!

He can have it! I give in!

Big Bad Barry was too big and too bad to become anyone's supper.
"We have to let him go," ordered Mr Elf. King Thistle let go of the fishing rod.

"Sorry we tried to catch you Barry," he laughed nervously.
Big Bad Barry ate the fishing rod in one bite.
"Aaagh!" yelled Mr Elf. "Now he's eating Bunty!"

"Launch the lifeboat!" cried Mr Elf.

Crunch! Crack!

Big Bad Barry had already munched through half of Bunty's deck!

The crew jumped ship in the nick of time. Mr Elf's boat was in pieces.

By the time the lifeboat floated to the shore, Nanny Plum was waiting. "The chips are ready," she announced. "Where's the fish?" Mr Elf shook his head. 'The fish' had just eaten Bunty.

Everybody looked at King Thistle. "I think I'd like fish fingers..." he said helpfully. "...with chips!" smiled Ben and Holly.

The End

Magic Jelly Boats

Poor old Mr Elf - he has lost a lot of boats to Big Bad Barry! The gigantic fish munches anything that dares to float on his lake.

Nanny Plum has decided to give Mr Elf a fairy helping hand. She's whipped up a spell for magic jelly boats! Would you like to make some too? The only things that are going to eat these boats are you and your friends!

Ingredients for a fleet of 16 jelly boats

* 4 oranges
* 2 packets of tangerine jelly
* blue food colouring
* 2 packets of strawberry jelly
* 1 can of squirty cream
* coloured paper
* cocktail sticks

Step 2

Put the two packs of tangerine jelly into a big jug and mix them up according to the packet instructions. Drip in a few drops of food colouring then stir the jelly mixture until it turns blue. Pour the jelly into a clear rectangular dish and pop it into the fridge to set.

Step 1

Ask a grown-up to help you cut the oranges into halves and scoop out the flesh

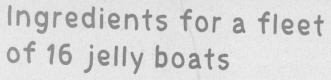

This will make a wobbly jelly lake for your boats to sail on!

Step 3

Line the orange halves up on a tray, then make up the packets of strawberry jelly. Pour the strawberry jelly into the empty oranges then put them in the fridge to set.

Step 4

When the jelly oranges are set, take them back out of the fridge. Ask a grown-up to cut each one in half to make a boat. Snip little rectangles out of coloured paper and push them through cocktail stick masts.

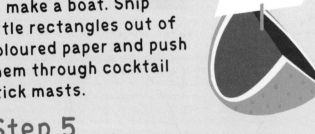

Step 5

Now take your jelly lake out. Spray the lake with a little squirty cream to make sea foam, then pop your magic jelly boats onto the water. Stay out of the way Big Bad Barry!

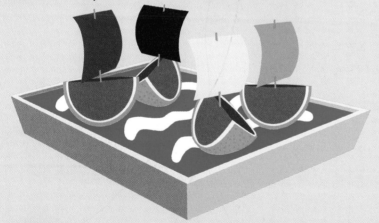

Always wash your hands and put on an apron before you start cooking. Magic jelly needs hot boiled water. Make sure that a grown-up is there to help you with all of the stages.

First there was Hilda, then...

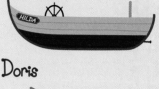

Doris

Peggy

Abigail

Fi

Trixibelle

Sabrina

Vicky

Miss
Boo
Boo

and

Bunty

... Barry ate them all!

65

Favourite Things

King Thistle mostly likes his newspaper, but Mr Elf likes boats, rockets and going to work. People really do like all sorts of funny things! Draw a line to match each person to the thing they like best.

What is your favourite thing? ....

Woodpecker Watch

King Thistle has got a new hobby - bird spotting! Today he looked out of the window and spotted a woodpecker. The bird has landed on the Great Elf Tree.

Take a peek through King Thistle's binoculars. What can he see? Now draw a circle around the things that have changed in the bottom picture. There are four differences to spot.

The Elf Factory

It was a snowy day in the Little Kingdom.

"It's a busy time of year for the elves," insisted Nanny Plum. "Christmas is coming up!."

"What's the plan for today Nanny Plum?" asked King Thistle at breakfast-time.

"You're visiting the Elf Factory," replied Nanny Plum. King Thistle didn't see the point.

Do I have to go?

The elves are expecting a royal visit.

The King and Queen decided Holly could go to the Elf Factory instead of the King, as long as Nanny Plum went too.

Hi Ben!

Hi Holly!

Ben Elf was pleased to see Holly and Nanny Plum. "Follow me!" smiled Ben.

Ben, Holly and Nanny Plum rode down a special escalator to a little room.
"Good morning," said a lady elf sitting behind a window.
"Can I help you?"
"This is the Elf Factory reception," explained Ben.

Holly and Nanny Plum were told to put on hard hats and hand in their wands. No magic was allowed in the factory.

Please make sure the dolls have a pretty red dress.

The Old Wise Elf rushed up to reception. to take a telephone call from Father Christmas.
"Ho ho ho!" said Father Christmas. "Will those dolls be ready in time for Christmas?"
"Yes," replied the Wise Old Elf.
"We're making hundreds of dolls," explained the Wise Old Elf. "They have to be ready today."

"This way," said the Wise Old Elf. "We'll be taking the train." Ben, Holly and Nanny Plum climbed into little orange carriages. "First stop level one, the computer room," announced the Wise Old Elf.

Hold on tight everyone!

Ooooh! Ooooh! Ooooh!

Nothing is left to chance.

"This is where we decide what the toys will look like," said the Wise Old Elf."It seems like a lot of hard work to me," whispered Nanny Plum.

The Wise Old Elf showed his visitors how a special computer set the colour of each toy.
"If I wanted to, I could change the doll's dress to blue," he said proudly.
"But Father Christmas wants a red dress," said Holly.
The Wise Old Elf nodded. "Of course."

Ben Elf told Holly and Nanny Plum
to get back on the train.
"We don't have to go down again
do we?" sighed Nanny Plum.
"Yes," smiled the Wise Old Elf.
"The Elf Factory is deep in the roots
of the tree."

The underground train went
faster... and faster... and FASTER!
"This is fun!" gasped Holly.
"Aarrgh!" screamed Nanny Plum.
"My tummy!"

Holly giggled.. The Elf Factory
was on level 99.
"This way," nodded the Wise Old Elf,
"feel free to ask any questions."
"Here's the gloop machine,"
added Ben.
Operating a gloop machine didn't
seem much fun.

"Don't you get bored?"
asked Nanny Plum.
"Elves never get bored,"
replied the machine operator.
"And I'm an elf!"

An elf was turning the gloop into doll shapes. "That's the moulding machine," explained Ben.

"You must be very patient," remarked Nanny Plum.
The moulding machine elf nodded. "Elves are very patient!"

Next, Ben led Holly into the paint room.
"This is where the toys are painted," said the Wise Old Elf.
"Every elf has a bit to paint."

The Wise Old Elf showed his guests how the dolls were painted, dried and then packed.
"A perfect example of elf workmanship," he said proudly.
"Isn't the doll's dress supposed to be red?" Holly asked.

The Wise Old Elf gasped. All the dolls had blue dresses!
"We'll have to unpack the dolls and paint them again," cried a painter elf.

"I could sort this out in a moment with a bit of magic," offered Nanny Plum.
What would Father Christmas say?
"Erm, maybe Nanny Plum can use a bit of magic," decided the Wise Old Elf.

Nanny Plum summoned her wand from reception.
"Blue to red," she said.
The first doll changed from blue to red, just like Nanny Plum had promised.

The elves found a chair for Nanny Plum. There were a LOT more dolls to get through.
"You must be so patient," grinned Ben.
"Yes Nanny Plum," winked the Wise Old Elf.
"We'll make an elf out of you yet!"

The End

73

The Big Farm

Ben and Holly have come to visit the Big Farm, but they need to be careful - big people have big feet! Luckily Lucy has arrived to show the fairies and elves around.

When it starts raining, Lucy has to get the animals into the barn. Gaston helps round everyone up. Even the Wise Old Elf agrees that he's a fine sheep-ladybird!

Take a look at the little pictures at the bottom of the page, then try and find each one in the big picture.

Colour in every one that you spot.

Lucy   Chicken   Flower

Bessie the cow

Sheep

Gaston

Goodnight Ben!

The moon is shining over the Little Kingdom. In the Great Elf Tree, Mrs Elf is reading Ben a storybook.

Colour in Ben and Mrs Elf in your favourite pencils or crayons.
Ben has done lots of painting today! Which picture do you like best?

Goodnight Holly!

King Thistle has already tucked in Daisy and Poppy. Now's it's Holly's bedtime. The princess is listening to an enchanting story about a fairy and an elf.

Colour in Holly and her pretty storybook. What shade will you choose for the cover?

Where does the fairy princess keep her crown when she goes to sleep?

Sleep well, Ben and Holly!

ZZZZZZZZZZZZZZZZZZZ

ANSWERS

Pages 8-9 Meet Ben!
Lots to learn at Elf School

1. Flying and spells are allowed in class. ✗
2. Lots of pictures are pinned up on the walls. ✓
3. The pupils sit at little wooden desks. ✓
4. The Wise Old Elf wears a funny pink hat. ✗
5. Elves learn to make clockwork owls, rabbits and robots. ✓

Pages 10-11 Meet Holly!
Magical Mix-ups

1. B
2. D
3. A
4. C

Pages 12-13 Meet Gaston!
Cave Counting

5 cobwebs
1 apple core
4 magazines
2 licked lollies
3 smelly socks

Gaston's food bowl is behind his bed.

Page 14 A Wander in the Woods
Mrs Witch

Pages 15 Musical Statues
D.

Pages 16-17 Meet King and Queen Thistle!
The royal fairy picnic

Pages 18-19 A Very Busy Day

Pages 28-29 Meet Daisy and Poppy!
Babies' bedtime

The colour of Daisy and Poppy's crowns is

The colour of the princess's bed is

The colour of their toybox is

The colour of Daisy and Poppy's duvet is

Pages 32-33 Chicken Run

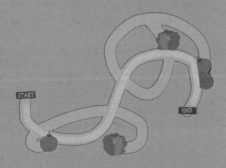

Pages 34-35 A Pet for the Princesses
B. A hamster is the smallest and fluffiest pet!

Page 36 Nature Class Quiz

1. b
2. a
3. a
4. c
5. a

Page 50 Alien Hide and Seek

Page 51 Space Trails
B

Page 66 Favourite Things

1. C
2. F
3. E
4. B
5. A
6. D

Page 67 Woodpecker Watch

WELL DONE!

78